LIKE A METAPHOR

A one-act dramedy by
Emily Cicchini

www.youthplays.com
info@youthplays.com
424-703-5315

COPYRIGHT RULES TO REMEMBER

CAST OF CHARACTERS

SCOUT, a girl who uses a wheelchair.

JAZZ, a boy who is always listening to music.

AMY and JAMIE, two girls in Scout's class who are highly concerned with fashion and style.

RICKY, a kid who hangs around with Jazz.

ANGEL, Scout's little sister.

DONNIS, a guy in the grade ahead of Scout, Class President.

They are in grades 6-9, ages 12-15.

SETTING

Kennedy Central School Cafeteria

Scout's Bedroom

Northtowne Mall

Kennedy Central School Library

Kennedy Central School Music Room

NOTE

The setting can be done quite simply, with iconic pieces representing place for quick transitions. The cafeteria is merely a long table with chairs or benches; Scout's bedroom, a cot covered with fluffy bedding; The Northtowne Mall can be a few potted plants and store advertisements; The library, a stack of books, or a short shelf full of them. The piano can be either electric or upright. A typical school room or auditorium can provide the backdrop to it all.

The focus of the play is the acting and the character relationships. It's important that Scout's wheelchair is real, fully functional, and up to date. It should be the kind of chair that a person in her situation would really use.

TIME

The Present.

(The lunch line in the Kennedy School cafeteria. Sounds of kids talking. A table with a stack of trays and plastic silverware and napkins is on the far stage right side. The wall is covered with posters: One says, "GO BLUEJAYS!" Another says "LADIES' CHOICE DANCE NEXT FRIDAY, TICKETS $10." Another says "PLEASE CLEAN UP AFTER YOURSELF. YOUR MOTHER DOESN'T WORK HERE." JAMIE, AMY, SCOUT, DONNIS, JAZZ and RICKY all stand in line, in that order, all facing stage right. Actually, Scout sits in line, in a slick wheelchair. There is a backpack hanging from the rear of her chair. There is a moment where they're all just waiting, but we can already see their personalities: what they are thinking about, what they are looking at, how they fidget. Jazz is listening to music through headphones. His body doesn't move at all to the beat, but sometimes, his lips do – silently. Jamie and Amy look around the room, whispering back and forth to each other. Scout follows their lead and inches closer.)

JAMIE: Look! Look at Tonya Quackenbush. What does she think she's wearing?

AMY: Is that feathers???

JAMIE: Is it pink? Or is it orange?

AMY: And her hair...

JAMIE: She's like a dead poodle!

(Amy and Jamie laugh and fall into each other, excluding Scout.)

SCOUT: I can't believe I forgot my lunch.

JAMIE: Don't worry about it, we'll help you.

SCOUT: It's not that, I just hate school food. What is it today, anyway?

DONNIS: Pizza. It's not so bad.

SCOUT: *(Turning her wheelchair slightly to look behind her:)* Oh. Hi.

DONNIS: Just pick off the mysterious meat pellets. I'm Donnis.

SCOUT: Yeah, I know.

JAMIE: Hi, Donnis.

AMY: Yeah, hi.

DONNIS: You're Scout, aren't you? When did you get back to school?

SCOUT: I guess it's been a couple of weeks...usually my mom packs my lunch...I keep it in my backpack, so I can just reach back and get it...

DONNIS: You're really brave.

SCOUT: You're really embarrassing.

DONNIS: I'm sorry. I'm just glad to see you're doing better.

SCOUT: Better than what?

JAMIE: Scout, Jeez! Donnis. Don't listen to her. She's doing fabulous. She's almost good as new, right Scout?

SCOUT: Yeah, right.

JAMIE: So Donnis. You going to the Ladies' Choice Dance?

DONNIS: Well, I don't know, Jamie. Nobody's asked me yet.

(From down the line, Ricky talks.)

RICKY: Are you ladies going to move it? We haven't got all day, you know.

JAMIE: Shut up, loser. We'll move when we're good and ready. *(She turns around and gets a tray:)* Come on, Amy.

AMY: *(Getting a tray for herself, and one for Scout:)* Here, Scout.

SCOUT: Um...

(Scout takes the tray in her hands, Jamie and Amy move forward and off stage. Scout looks down at her wheels, with her hands full.)

Uh, Amy?

RICKY: What's the hold up now???

DONNIS: Can I, I mean, may I help you?

SCOUT: Sure. Thanks.

(Donnis starts to push her wheelchair.)

You know what? I'm not crazy about being pushed. It kind of makes me seasick.

DONNIS: How about I take your tray, and we just put everything on mine. Then I'll bring it to your table.

SCOUT: That would be great, thanks. Thanks a lot.

(Scout hands her tray to Donnis, and moves forward in line. Suddenly, Jazz starts singing out loud, totally into the music. Donnis and Scout look over at Jazz like he's crazy.)

JAZZ: Ba-da-da, Ba-da-da, DA DA DA, Ba-da-da, da-da-da, deddle, deddle deet...

(Ricky taps Jazz's shoulder.)

RICKY: Man. Jazz. Man!

JAZZ: *(Pulling off his headphones, a little too wildly:)* Don't touch me!

RICKY: Sorry, Jazz. *(Holding his hands up with palms open:)* I had to. Your volume was turned on.

JAZZ: What?

RICKY: *(Spelling it out for him slowly:)* Your volume. You know. Your real volume.

JAZZ: Oh. Right. *(Looking over at Donnis and Scout:)* Sorry. *(To Ricky:)* Thanks, Ricky.

RICKY: No problemo, Jazzmo.

JAZZ: *(Looking at Scout:)* Are you paralyzed? Forever?

DONNIS: What the — how can you ask a question like that?

SCOUT: It's okay, Donnis. Yes. Yes I am. Unless they find a cure.

JAZZ: Stem cell research.

SCOUT: Maybe.

JAZZ: You're paraplegic. You can use your arms.

SCOUT: Yes, that's right.

JAZZ: A quadriplegic can't use their arms.

SCOUT: No. But some of them use their mouths. To write. Or paint. Or play music, even.

(Jazz puts on his headphones again, and seems to go someplace else.)

DONNIS: Come on, Scout. Let's check out that pizza.

SCOUT: Still sounds scary to me. But let's go.

(Scout wheels herself out, followed by Donnis. Jazz moves forward slowly behind. Ricky calls out.)

RICKY: He doesn't mean to be rude! *(Almost to himself:)* It's just the way he is.

(Jazz and Ricky exit. Jazz music plays while the setting is changed from the cafeteria to Scout's bedroom: Posters of

current music and television stars on the walls. A chair with some clothes draped over it. As this is happening, Scout comes forward and talks directly to the audience.)

SCOUT: My name is Scout. It's my real name, not a nickname. I'm named after the main character in the book *To Kill a Mockingbird* by Harper Lee. It was my mother's favorite. I didn't like my name very much when I was growing up, because it just doesn't sound like a girl's name. When I was recovering from the accident, my mother gave me a copy of the book. I have to say, it changed my mind. *To Kill a Mockingbird* is the first real "adult" book I ever read, and it's just, well, it's amazing, you know? I don't even want to try to explain it, because it's better if you read it yourself. It's like trying to explain what it's like to be paralyzed. But the main thing is, it taught me to appreciate metaphors. Metaphors are when you use words to paint a picture that means many things at once...like "apple of my eye," or "raining cats and dogs" or "so hot you could fry an egg." *To Kill a Mockingbird* means a lot of things. It's about racism and discrimination. It's about growing up. Killing a mockingbird is sort of like, doing something wrong to someone who is innocent. See, a metaphor makes the words work harder.

(There is a knock at the door.)

ANGEL: *(Offstage:)* Scout?   ·

SCOUT: That's my sister, Angel. I guess my parents figured out by the time she came along how to really name a girl. *(Calling:)* Come in!

(ANGEL comes in with her suitcase.)

ANGEL: I can't decide what to bring with me.

SCOUT: Bring what you normally bring.

ANGEL: But this time we're going to the country. There's supposed to be horseback riding and swimming...

SCOUT: Isn't it a little cold for swimming?

ANGEL: It's an indoor pool. It's Veronica's family. She's rich, you know.

SCOUT: So I've heard. But not rich enough to put a ramp on their house.

ANGEL: It's not about the money, Scout. They said the neighborhood won't approve the plans.

SCOUT: That's discrimination.

ANGEL: Dad's going to talk to them about it.

SCOUT: Yeah, right. Next year. Right after they widen their bathroom doors.

ANGEL: I'm sorry you don't get to go stay with Dad, Scout. It's not fair.

SCOUT: It wasn't fair that he left Mom, either.

ANGEL: He's happier now. And Veronica's not that bad.

SCOUT: Whatever, Angel. What do you want, anyway?

ANGEL: I was wondering...can I borrow your bathing suit? The blue bikini?

SCOUT: But I was planning on wearing it to physical therapy! *(Pause.)* I'm kidding! It's over on the chair. I can't wear a bikini anymore, with all the scars...

ANGEL: Are these your brown suede cropped pants? Oh, wouldn't I look so fine riding Victoria's English pony in these...

SCOUT: Take them.

ANGEL: No. They're your favorite...

SCOUT: They're too hard to get on anymore. I wish I could have ridden a horse like that.

ANGEL: But you can, right? There isn't a law against it...

SCOUT: Even if they did help me get up on the horse, I'll never be able to...what do they call it? Post. You know. Move up and down with your legs, as you ride, like in the movies, like *National Velvet*... It just wouldn't be right, you know?

ANGEL: I'm sorry I brought it up.

SCOUT: No, are you kidding me? It's amazing that you get to ride her horses. Go, have a good time, okay? Take the pants. Take anything you want.

ANGEL: Thanks, Scout. I'll take good care of them, I promise.

(Angel leaves.)

SCOUT: Dad left about a month before the accident. In some ways, I was relieved, not to hear them fighting all the time. He got remarried before I even left the hospital, to some woman he'd just met. I guess she's a lawyer. I didn't even meet her until after I was released. The arrangement is that Angel goes to stay with them every other weekend. Every other Wednesday, they come and take me out to dinner. I have to make suggestions, because a couple of times they've taken me to places that are completely inaccessible...some fancy place up some flight of stairs with no elevator. It's like, Dad doesn't want to admit his daughter is a cripple. Cripple is one of those bad words you shouldn't say in public. I would get angry if someone called me that to my face. But when I say it myself, it kind of helps me own it.

(Music again, something they would play over a loudspeaker in a store. Scout rolls off stage. The setting changes to Northtowne

Mall. Signs that say popular store names and "SALE" and "20% OFF" and "NEW SHIPMENT" and "ONE DAY ONLY." Amy and Jamie come on, with shopping bags in their hand. Scout follows. Amy and Jamie sit on a bench.)

JAMIE: I am so glad I found that matching top. I was afraid I was going to have to throw that skirt away.

AMY: It looks great on you, Jamie.

SCOUT: Let me see it!

(Jamie pulls it out of the bag and gives it to Scout.)

JAMIE: It's such a shame you couldn't come in the dressing room. It looks much different on.

SCOUT: Oh, it's nice!

(Jamie grabs it back and puts it back in her bag.)

JAMIE: So. I still can't decide who to ask to the Ladies' Choice Dance. Luis or Michael.

AMY: Luis is better looking.

JAMIE: Yeah, but Michael has a better body.

SCOUT: I was thinking...maybe I'll ask Donnis to the dance.

JAMIE: What! Are you crazy?

AMY: Why would you want to go to a dance, anyway?

JAMIE: Amy, don't be stupid. Scout can go to the dance if she wants. People don't have to dance to go to a dance.

SCOUT: Who says I can't dan—

JAMIE: The point is...Donnis is way out of your league, Scout. He's older than us. He's popular, too. He's even class president!

SCOUT: Yeah, you're probably right.

JAMIE: Oh look at that dress in the window. Let's go in there...

SCOUT: That's a cheap store...

JAMIE: I've found good things in there...

AMY: Sure, so have I.

SCOUT: Well, maybe it's not so cheap...but...just look, the way they've got it arranged...

JAMIE: It looks kinda cute to me...

AMY: Yeah, very metro, very downtown...

SCOUT: It's all crowded in there. I don't think I'll even fit between the racks...

JAMIE: That's okay. You can just wait out here for us.

SCOUT: Oh, you want me to wait for you?

JAMIE: Sure, you don't mind, do you?

SCOUT: No. Why would I mind?

AMY: Will you watch our bags?

SCOUT: I — um — Sure.

> (*Amy and Jamie dump off their bags next to Scout and exit. Scout turns to the audience:*)

Amy and Jamie are my best friends. I've known them since third grade, when we moved here from Lincoln. We used to have sleep-overs every weekend and make up these weird things to eat with sugar and cinnamon and crackers and butter all hot and melted into candy. But we haven't slept over since the accident. When it first happened, they were right there, by my side, every day. I mean, they cried, they brought me all kinds of flowers and magazines and things, and they were really, really great. But since I've been back at school, I don't know. Something's changed. It's like, I'm just annoying to them. I can't stand to feel that way. See, the deal is, I am different, too. I just don't really care about the same things that I used to. Clothes. Music. The next hottest thing doesn't matter anymore. I'm looking for something...something more, classic, now, more timeless, more real. Authentic. Maybe...maybe that's, you know what they say, the silver lining. The silver lining to losing the use of your legs. Everything just gets, a little, slower, you know? It's given me time to stop and smell the roses.

(Jazz enters, followed by Ricky. He starts to go up to Scout.)

JAZZ: Look. It's that girl. From school.

RICKY: Hold it. What are you doing, brother?

JAZZ: I'm going to ask her where the music store is.

RICKY: Come on, I told you, man, I can find the music store. It's not like I've never been to the Northtowne Mall before...

JAZZ: It's been seventeen minutes and twenty-eight seconds. I don't think you know where the music store is.

RICKY: Man! What do you think I am, stupid? I can find the dang music store...this place is just so big...

JAZZ: Excuse me.

SCOUT: Oh, hi.

JAZZ: Do you know where the music store is?

SCOUT: Um, I think it's over that way.

JAZZ: South by southwest.

SCOUT: I guess so. See, the blue sign?

JAZZ: Past the pothos ivy and split leaf philodendrons.

SCOUT: You mean the potted plants?

JAZZ: Yes.

SCOUT: You know a lot, don't you?

JAZZ: About some things. Not so much about others.

RICKY: Jazz is a genius. He's amazing. You should hear him play piano...

JAZZ: No! She's a stranger!

RICKY: Calm down, calm down. He only lets certain people hear him play. People he already knows.

SCOUT: Well, Jazz, my name is Scout.

JAZZ: Scout. Like in the book by Harper Lee. *To Kill a Mockingbird*.

SCOUT: Yes. Exactly!

JAZZ: I don't like that book.

SCOUT: You've read it?

JAZZ: Too many metaphors.

   (Amy and Jamie enter.)

JAMIE: Scout! Come on. We've got to get going...

AMY: Yeah, my mom is picking us up, and you know how long it takes to get your chair folded up and in the trunk...

RICKY: We've got to get going, too.

JAZZ: Bye, Scout.

SCOUT: Bye.

   (Jazz and Ricky exit.)

JAMIE: Were you talking to those "special needs" kids?

AMY: That Jazz guy is psycho or something. He sits in the front of my math class just doing problem after problem after problem, sometimes he runs out of paper and keeps writing on the desk and the teacher has to stop him...

SCOUT: They asked for directions to the music store. That's all.

JAMIE: Scout. You've got to be careful. You're not like them. You don't want people thinking that you're special ed or something...

SCOUT: I can't believe you just said that.

JAMIE: I'm sorry, but I'm just worried about your reputation.

SCOUT: I think you're more worried about your own.

AMY: Scout. How can you say that? Doesn't our friendship mean anything to you?

SCOUT: Of course it does. Of course. I'm sorry. We better get going. We don't want to keep your mother waiting.

(Scout, Amy, and Jamie exit. The MUSIC changes to classic Jazz. Maybe John Coltraine or Miles Davis. The signs change again: QUIET. NO TALKING. FICTION/NON-FICTION, with arrows pointing in different directions. A table comes on with an old record player and big old clunky headphones. Jazz is listening to music, and looking at an album cover, that reads, LEGENDS IN JAZZ. Scout wheels in with some books on her lap. She sees Jazz, thinks about it for a moment, and then goes over to him. She starts to reach out and touch him...but then decides against it. She pulls out a book, and puts it right in front of his eyes, between the album cover and his face. He looks at the book, and she pulls the book over back on her lap. His eyes follow it, and then go up to her face.)

JAZZ: Oh, hello...

(He takes off the headphones quickly. The MUSIC stops.)

SCOUT: Am I bothering you?

JAZZ: No...I was just listening...to some great music. You can't even get this anywhere. I've tried.

SCOUT: You really like jazz music, don't you?

JAZZ: It's the only thing that helps me relax. Why are you talking to me?

SCOUT: I don't know. I like music too.

JAZZ: I've never talked to a girl before. I mean, other than my mother.

SCOUT: That's okay. I won't bite.

JAZZ: You mean, like a dog?

SCOUT: Yes.

JAZZ: Bite like a dog. That's a simile. I like similes.

SCOUT: What do you mean?

JAZZ: Similes are where you say something is LIKE something. Or sometimes you can use AS. Sly as a fox. Like father, like son. That makes sense to me. It's true. Some fathers are like some sons. But metaphors...that's when people say something IS something else. That's confusing. That's just a lie.

SCOUT: I remember. You said you didn't like *To Kill a Mockingbird*, because it had too many metaphors.

JAZZ: People say...for instance...love is blind. Love is an emotion, it doesn't have eyes, so it can't see in the first place. So how can it be blind? When people use metaphors, I have to go through all that translation to make it real, and it gives me a pain in my brain.

SCOUT: You think differently, you're saying.

JAZZ: The doctors call it autism. My mother calls it Asperger's syndrome. She says she likes the way it sounds better. I call it neurologically diverse.

SCOUT: Gosh. Wow. Shouldn't you be sitting in a corner rocking back or forth or something?

JAZZ: Only when I'm having a really bad day. *(Beat.)* That was a joke. I don't rock. I do stack and count things, like the number of tiles on the ceiling. There's 247 in this room. 1,523 in the cafeteria.

SCOUT: Wow. Funny. You know, you were the first person at school to use the word paralyzed around me. And to ask me if it was permanent.

JAZZ: I'm sorry.

SCOUT: No, don't be! I like that I can finally be honest with someone. Everyone around me puts on this niccy nicey attitude, it's really annoying.

JAZZ: Like that Donnis guy?

SCOUT: I wasn't really talking about him...

JAZZ: Are you going to ask him to the dance?

SCOUT: I guess that's none of your business.

JAZZ: I don't even want to go to the dance. See, there is this jazz quartet playing that same night, at this club called The Oasis...

SCOUT: The Oasis? Isn't that a bar or something?

JAZZ: It's an "all-ages" show. But my parents won't let me go. They won't let me go anywhere alone. Sometimes...sometimes I get confused.

SCOUT: Oh. That's too bad. What about that friend of yours?

JAZZ: He can't. He's got something at his church he has to do. This is the only time they've ever come here. They're from Chicago. That's the only night they're playing.

SCOUT: Maybe your parents will take you.

JAZZ: My father is not like his son.

(The school bell rings.)

SCOUT: Well, I better get going. You know, one thing I've learned about this condition is it takes me a little longer to get from place to place. I have to allow extra time for everything. I'll see you around, okay?

JAZZ: Yes. You'll see me. I'll see you.

(Sound of talking returns. The signs from the cafeteria return, with one new one: ONLY 20 MORE TICKETS LEFT FOR THE LADIES CHOICE DANCE! BUY SOON OR LOSE! A table and chairs come in. Lunch is on the table. Jamie and Amy pick at their food. Scout eats from her lunchbag.)

AMY: I'm thinking about getting my hair straightened. What do you think?

SCOUT: I like your hair how it is, Amy...

JAMIE: Do it. And you should think about color, too. Maybe blond, or red!

SCOUT: Jamie, you've been through so many colors now, that how do you expect anybody to ever recognize you?

JAMIE: Who are you to give me any advice about hairstyle, Scout? If I remember correctly, you were shaved bald not so long ago.

AMY: Oooooh!

SCOUT: I'm just kidding, Jamie. I love your hair, really. And you know that bald head wasn't really my choice.

(Donnis comes by.)

DONNIS: What's up?

JAMIE: Hi Donnis! Luis and I are going to the dance...

AMY: And I'm going with Justin...

JAMIE: Wanna sit with us?

DONNIS: Well, I would, but I still don't know who I'm going with. Let me go get some eats and maybe you can figure it out for me. I'll be right back.

(Donnis leaves.)

SCOUT: I'm going to ask him.

JAMIE: Don't do it.

SCOUT: I think he wants me to ask him. He's always dropping hints.

AMY: Listen to Jamie. She just wants the best for you...

SCOUT: Maybe I'm not the same as I was outside, but I'm just the same inside. If I could still walk you would be thrilled about me asking Donnis to go to the dance. Are you ashamed of me, or something?

JAMIE: It's not us. It's him. Don't you see? Donnis is just coming on to you because it's good for his image. He wants everyone to see him being nice to the girl in the wheelchair, so he can gain more sympathy and win more votes.

SCOUT: What?

JAMIE: Hello, it's election time.

SCOUT: You're awful, Jamie. I don't believe it. I'm going to ask him anyway.

JAMIE: Well, I can't be here to watch you make a fool out of yourself. We love you, Scout, but we don't want to see you get hurt. Come on, Amy.

(Jamie and Amy leave together.)

SCOUT: Nothing could hurt more than the way they were treating me. I knew right then they weren't my friends anymore.

(Donnis comes back with his tray.)

DONNIS: What's up with them?

SCOUT: Um, they had to go to class. Um...Donnis? I was wondering. Do you...want to go...to the dance...with me?

DONNIS: I thought you'd never ask.

SCOUT: REALLY? That's great. That's—amazing. That's—unbelievable!

(Donnis looks around, to see who might be watching them.)

What are you looking at?

DONNIS: Nothing, nothing. *(He finally looks back at her, and holds her hand:)* I'm just glad to see you happy. You deserve it.

(Donnis and Scout exit. The set changes back to Scout's bedroom. MUSIC plays, something popular that Scout might listen to. She is recording a diary entry.)

SCOUT: Mom was driving when it happened. We were coming back from dropping Angel off at dance class. I just went along for the ride, for no reason. It was a perfectly normal day. We were crossing the intersection at Washington, and this truck came out of nowhere. Ran the red light.

Slammed right into the passenger side. I never even saw it coming. I hardly even felt a thing. Until I woke up three days later. Then, it was pain like you can't describe: pain is an excellent teacher. Mom was standing over me: she was fine, thank goodness, hardly hurt at all, just a scratch on her forehead. She said, "He was drunk. What were they thinking, letting a drunk man drive their truck..." I think both she and Angel somehow feel responsible, in their own ways. Even though I tell them over and over..."it was just an accident! How could we have known?"

(Angel knocks at the door again.)

ANGEL: *(Offstage:)* Scout? Can I come in?

SCOUT: Sure, sis.

(Scout does. She's wearing brown pants.)

Those pants look great on you.

ANGEL: Scout. I have to tell you something.

SCOUT: Oh, sounds serious. Let me sit down. Oh, right. I am sitting down.

ANGEL: Very funny. I don't want to go to Dad's house anymore.

SCOUT: Angel, don't say that. Just because I can't—

ANGEL: Listen to me. I found out something. About Victoria.

SCOUT: What?

ANGEL: You know, when they had the hearing, and the judge found that the police had messed up on the breathalyzer test, and they let that trucker go?

SCOUT: Yes. It sucked. What does this have to do with Victoria?

ANGEL: She was that guy's lawyer, Scout. Victoria let the man that did this to you go free.

SCOUT: Are you sure?

ANGEL: I was in her office. I saw the file. And then I asked Mom about it. She said it was true.

SCOUT: How...how could Daddy marry a person like that?

ANGEL: I confronted him about it. He said...she was just doing her job. It had nothing to do with who she was.

SCOUT: I—I don't know what to say.

ANGEL: He let us down, Scout. He's still letting us down. Mom says we don't have to go there anymore. She says she'll find another lawyer, one that's better than Victoria.

SCOUT: Okay. Okay.

ANGEL: I—I love you, Scout.

SCOUT: I love you too, Angel.

ANGEL: Tell Mom I'll be out to help with dinner in just a bit, okay?

SCOUT: Okay.

(Angel leaves.)

Before the accident, I took dance lessons, too. I loved to dance, hip hop, African, modern, even ballet. I thought maybe, someday, I'd be a dancer...maybe in videos, behind the lead singer...or commercials on TV...

(Music returns. She begins to dance with the music with her upper body.)

I could bust a move with the best of them, shaking my wild thang, feeling like I could slice the air like butter, I was a house on fire.

(She moves her head and upper body to the music, gracefully and full of meaning. Donnis suddenly enters. The MUSIC changes to something slow.)

DONNIS: May I have this dance?

SCOUT: Donnis—what are you doing in my bedroom? Am I dreaming?

DONNIS: Haven't you had this fantasy before?

SCOUT: Oh, yes—I guess I have.

(He walks towards her. She looks up at him. He reaches out a hand to her, as if to help her to her feet. She takes it, as if to stand up, right out of the chair. Just as she starts to:)

Wait. Something...something's not right.

(She falls back in her seat. Donnis shakes his head, a little condescendingly. He squats down, as if he might try to pick her up.)

DONNIS: Get up. Get up on your feet and dance with me.

SCOUT: I...I can't, Donnis.

DONNIS: Don't say that. You can do anything that you put your mind to.

SCOUT: I can do a lot of things, just, not that.

DONNIS: I don't want to hear that kind of talk. You can get better again. They are making great progress with science. You will walk again, someday...

SCOUT: I don't want to spend my life waiting for someday. I don't want to feel like I'm not okay right now, just how I am...

DONNIS: Don't give up on yourself, Scout. You're so brave.

SCOUT: I'm not that brave. I get scared all the time.

DONNIS: It's not fair. I want you to be well again. You deserve to be happy.

SCOUT: I don't deserve to be happy any more than any other person, Donnis. I'm just a person. A person who uses a wheelchair.

DONNIS: Come on, now. Stand up!

(*He tries to lift her to her feet. She struggles to get away, to stay down. He tries again, despite her protests.*)

SCOUT: No! I can't walk, Donnis. I don't even want to pretend that I can.

(*He stumbles, and falls back.*)

I want to be okay with who I am right now, not who I used to be...even in my dreams.

(*Donnis exits. JAZZ MUSIC plays. Solo piano. New signs, maybe on a blackboard: DO, RA, ME, FA, SO, LA, TE, DO; SPRING CONCERT TENTATIVE DATE: MAY 1. Jazz sits at a piano. It can be an electric piano or upright. Jazz sits behind it, playing, totally engrossed in playing the music. Scout enters. Jazz stops playing.*)

Don't stop. You're amazing. Unbelievable.

JAZZ: It makes me nervous to play in front of people.

SCOUT: But music soothes the savage beast, right?

JAZZ: I am not a beast.

SCOUT: I know, it's just another metaphor. And in this case, I'm the beast.

(Ricky enters.)

RICKY: Huh. Oh. It's you again. Is she bothering you, Jazz?

JAZZ: No. She is not bothering me.

RICKY: Cause I'll get rid of her, if you want me to.

SCOUT: I won't be long. I was thinking of signing up for choir next year. I thought I'd talk to the teacher about it...

RICKY: There are risers in choir. Where are they going to put you, right smack on the floor?

SCOUT: Maybe, if they have to.

JAZZ: Ricky, why don't you just...go away...and get a life.

(Scout bursts out laughing.)

RICKY: What? What's so funny?

SCOUT: Jazz! You just used a metaphor!

JAZZ: What?

SCOUT: When you said "get a life," you didn't literally mean that Ricky was dead. You meant he didn't have an interesting life. One of his own.

RICKY: Hey. Should I be offended by that?

JAZZ: I'm just saying, leave us alone.

RICKY: Fine, if that's what you want. No respect. I get no respect.

(Ricky exits.)

SCOUT: See, I think your brain can handle more metaphors than maybe you've been letting on. And...Ricky's not the only one who needs to get a life. Maybe I do, too.

JAZZ: What do you mean? You're not dying, are you?

SCOUT: No. But I think I'm going to have to nip something in the bud.

(Donnis enters.)

DONNIS: There you are, Scout. I've been looking all over for you. I wanted to make sure that I'm prepared enough for the dance. I've ordered an accessible limo...

SCOUT: Donnis. Wait a minute. I want you to tell me something. And be honest with me.

DONNIS: Of course...

SCOUT: Would you be going to this dance with me if I didn't use this wheelchair?

DONNIS: What?

SCOUT: Would you even know who I was if I hadn't have been in the accident?

DONNIS: I don't understand. What are you saying?

SCOUT: What is it, exactly, that you like about me.

DONNIS: Um... (Noticing Jazz, who is still there, watching:) Maybe this isn't the time or place...

SCOUT: Name one thing.

DONNIS: I don't know, I...

SCOUT: Can't you do better than that?

DONNIS: I think—I think you're a kind of a hero, acting like it doesn't bother you.

SCOUT: Like what, like what doesn't bother me?

DONNIS: That you can't walk. That you'll probably never walk again. I mean, most people would fall apart, or get angry, or even want to die. I mean, it's a terrible, sad thing that happened to you, Scout. It's a tragedy. But you, you're still funny, even nice...

SCOUT: I'm not a tragic hero, Donnis. I'm just a girl who got in an accident. Don't you understand that? *(Pause.)* I really don't want your pity, okay?

DONNIS: What are you saying?

SCOUT: I think—maybe...we shouldn't go to the dance.

DONNIS: Are you...dissing me?

SCOUT: I'm sorry, Donnis. I just don't think it's right.

DONNIS: I don't understand. I'm just trying to help you.

SCOUT: See, I don't really need that much help. What I really need is a friend.

DONNIS: Okay. Fine. Have fun. Maybe you two freaks belong together.

(Donnis exits.)

JAZZ: Did he literally call us freaks?

SCOUT: Yes, he literally did.

JAZZ: I'm not sure I understand what just happened.

SCOUT: I think I just saved a mockingbird: me. You know what I've been thinking, Jazz? That your music, jazz music, it's sort of like a metaphor. It's not all cut and dried and put together like a lot of music. It's more like emotion...it kind of goes all over the place, and it means many things at once.

JAZZ: People have so many emotions, and it's hard for me to know what they really mean when they talk.

SCOUT: I feel the same way sometimes. And I'm not even autistic. Jazz, do you still want to go to the Oasis?

JAZZ: Of course. But my parents...the Ladies' Choice Dance...

SCOUT: Listen. I want my mom to take us. Both of us. This isn't a date or anything, we're just going to see some music. Do you think your parents would let you go then?

JAZZ: I don't know for sure. But I expect they would say yes.

SCOUT: So we'll do it.

JAZZ: Amazing. Unbelievable.

SCOUT: My mom needs to drive me someplace again. She hasn't done it since the accident. I take public transportation and a cab or get rides from other people. It's a big pain, and that needs to change. It will be good for her, and you'll get to see that quartet from Chicago...and who knows. Maybe I'll even dance a little.

JAZZ: But how can you dance? It's jazz...people can't dance to jazz...

SCOUT: Brother, watch me dance. I can dance like a mockingbird sings!

> *(Jazz begins to play again. Scout moves her wheelchair back and forth with one arm, and lifts her other arm high in the air, moving it to his music. She moves more and more. Scout slips down, out of her chair, to the floor. She pushes the chair away. She is dancing abstractly on the floor, mirroring the highs and lows of the music with her arms and face, her legs still paralyzed, laughing. Jazz watches, and laughs, too.)*

The Author Speaks

What inspired you to write this play?
I was doing arts integration with a variety of people with disabilities when Boston Public Schools came out with a call to write a play for middle school actors to perform. I wanted to try to capture the idea of inclusion and respect for people of all abilities and share it with young performers, particularly at this really challenging adolescent age of tweens, so that they could come to see how being different isn't always bad. So, I wrote the play specifically for their contest, and was thrilled when it was selected.

Was the structure of the play influenced by any other work?
I was thinking a bit about Tennessee Williams' *Glass Menagerie*, how Laura is such a victim, and what a negative stereotype that is, in comparison to the people with disabilities I have known. But I do like the structure of "The Memory Play," where there is an active narrator who can put certain elements of the story into historical perspective. Also, *To Kill a Mockingbird* is clearly referenced, partly because the character of Boo Radley is representative of the innocence and isolation of people with disability; and also, the idea of killing a mockingbird is a really terrific example of the power of metaphor vs. a simple simile.

Have you dealt with the same theme in other works that you have written?
I am very interested in people's flaws. I think we're all flawed, in some way; and yet, often that flaw is somehow related to our greatest strength. I'm also often concerned about what is normal, about wanting to feel normal, when in reality, I think no one is perfectly normal. I have dealt with these issues in at least one other play, *A Dragon's Happy Day*, that was

commissioned and presented by The Pollyanna Theatre Company, where I'm playwright in residence. In that play, there is a dragon, Brain, who has, in effect, Attention Deficit Hyperactivity Disorder. The fire he spits out is a manifestation of the loss of self-control that some people with this condition experience. One of the hardest things about writing about disability is the urge to label things, to make the conditions clear. But in both my writing and my personal experience, disabilities are never totally independent or clear cut. People want labels, because it makes the situation more understandable, digestible, controllable. But part of the beauty of individuality, of disability as well as special abilities, is the mystery of what exactly they are and how they are manifested in the things we say and do.

What writers have had the most profound effect on your style?
Playwright Suzan Zeder has been a huge influence on me. She was one of my most influential teachers. She had a very interesting way of approaching play structure, influenced by non-linear storytelling and extensive use of metaphor and imagery. She assigned us to express our play in different ways; like a sculpture, or a song, or a tarot deck and do a fortune telling of it. She was really demanding about re-writing and re-writing and more re-writing! Afterwards, I got a bit more methodical in my structure. I like to make outlines and charts and graphs of character motivations and obstacles. I'm drawn to well-made social plays, like Ibsen and Chekhov and Brecht. And Shakespeare, of course. He's amazing for creating scenes without settings, you know; through entrances, exits, and beautiful but judicious exposition. I'm also fond of more contemporary writers John Olive and Eric Overmyer, Sarah Ruhl and Lisa D'Amour.

What do you hope to achieve with this work?

I hope that it helps people be open-minded and compassionate, particularly people with obvious (and sometimes hidden) differences. I hope that some young actors feel challenged and enjoy performing in this play, and that audiences have good discussions about disability and friendship after seeing it. I hope it removes some fear and prejudice about disability.

What are the most common mistakes that occur in productions of your work?

I'm not that great at writing stage directions, so people sometimes don't understand how much physical interaction I see happening in my scripts. I got too much criticism for writing cinematically in my early plays, and getting too much in the way of the director...so, I stopped paying a lot of attention to setting and action, and tried just to focus on the sound of the dialogue and the emotional lives of the characters. Then, the actors and director and designers can work out how it should be staged. It's great to be a resident playwright, because I have a relationship with Dr. Judy Matetzschk-Campbell that allows us to shorthand a lot of the stage details. I was a little more careful with this play, however, to describe the action, because I knew I wouldn't be intimately involved with the productions.

What inspired you to become a playwright?

I just love playing and storytelling and imagination, getting lost in another world, often with others. I was always torn between acting and writing growing up. As I got older, it became more practical to be a playwright, because it was something you could do anytime, anywhere, even without an audience or a theatre production (at least at first). But that's the drawback to being a playwright; it can take a very long time sometimes between the moments when you as a writer are swept away in the drama, and when you get to share that with an audience. But when it does happen, it's a pretty magical experience. I love it when an audience is moved by, humored by, and otherwise seems to enjoy my plays. I think there is a special experience of truth of human connection when it all finally comes together. It's very spiritual for me, being part of an audience of a play I've written. I'm suddenly not so alone. People understand me, and I understand them better, too; audience, director, actors, and the characters we've created, together. It's transcendent.

How did you research the subject?
When I wrote this play, I was spending days with young children with autism in schools, and helping to support some nighttime public performances of a troupe of older actors and dancers and poets and singers with a variety of physical disabilities; traumatic head injury, paralysis, deafness, and a variety of other "labels of disability" (Actual Lives). I was struck at how all these people refused to be pitied; they really just wanted to express themselves and have fun and be accepted and be themselves, exactly who there were, right there and then. It was such a profound sense of dignity. I helped me to understand the people in my life with disabilities better, and my own mixed feelings about them. It has helped me prepare for times when I myself became disabled, which happens to one out of five Americans during their lifetime; even just times of sickness or temporary trauma. And to fear it just a bit less.

Are any characters modeled after real life or historical figures?
There is a terrific book called *The Curious Incident of the Dog in the Night-Time* by Mark Haddon that was very much the

model for Jazz. I was also really impressed by the young jazz performer Matt Savage, who has a form of autism called pervasive developmental disorder. Scout was inspired by a number of dancers I've known who used wheelchairs or other mobility aids, such as Axis Dance Company, and independent teaching artist Jaehn Clare, whose help on the script was invaluable. I think it was Jaehn who encouraged me not to have Scout break the reality of her disability by standing up to dance in the dream sequence; but to stay dancing with paralysis on the floor. That was certainly more true to the way I'd seen dance like this performed, and is really much more on point to the theme of the play.

Shakespeare gave advice to the players in *Hamlet*; if you could give advice to your cast what would it be?
Listen to each other when you act. Don't plan out exactly what you're going to do or sound like; let the truth come out of each moment through your honest reaction, and the reality of the situation for the character that you are playing.

About the Author

Emily Cicchini writes material for stage, film and interactive media, most notably ***Becoming Brontë*** and ***Mays & Terese***. Her work has been honored with the Austin Critics' Table Award for Best Original New Script, the B. Iden Payne Award for Outstanding Original Script, and by the Children's Foundation of America. As resident playwright since the company's inception, the Pollyanna Theatre Company has premiered many of her original plays for young audiences, including ***Edward, The Owl, and The Calico Cat***, ***A Christmas Rose***, ***Community Helpers on Wheels***, ***A Dragon's Happy Day***, ***Duckie Sees The World***, ***Just Bee***, and the ***Pattern Nation*** series. She edited the four-volume Mother/Daughter

Monologues series for the International Centre for Women Playwrights. Cicchini holds an MFA in playwriting from the University of Texas at Austin where she wa a James A. Michener Fellow, and a BFA in acting from DePaul/Goodman School of Drama. See more at www.emilycicchini.com.

About YouthPLAYS

YouthPLAYS (www.youthplays.com) is a publisher of award-winning professional dramatists and talented new discoveries, each with an original theatrical voice, and all dedicated to expanding the vocabulary of theatre for young actors and audiences. On our website you'll find one-act and full-length plays and musicals for teen and pre-teen (and even college) actors, as well as duets and monologues for competition. Many of our authors' works have been widely produced at high schools and middle schools, youth theatres and other TYA companies, both amateur and professional, as well as at elementary schools, camps, churches and other institutions serving young audiences and/or actors worldwide. Most are intended for performance by young people, while some are intended for adult actors performing for young audiences.

YouthPLAYS was co-founded by professional playwrights Jonathan Dorf and Ed Shockley. It began merely as an additional outlet to market their own works, which included a substantial body of award-winning published and unpublished plays and musicals. Those interested in their published plays were directed to the respective publishers' websites, and unpublished plays were made available in electronic form. But when they saw the desperate need for material for young actors and audiences—coupled with their experience that numerous quality plays for young people weren't finding a home—they made the decision to represent the work of other playwrights as well. Dozens and dozens of authors are now members of the YouthPLAYS family, with scripts available both electronically and in traditional acting editions. We continue to grow as we look for exciting and challenging plays and musicals for young actors and audiences.

About ProduceaPlay.com

Let's put up a play! Great idea! But producing a play takes time, energy and knowledge. While finding the necessary time and energy is up to you, ProduceaPlay.com is a website designed to assist you with that third element: knowledge.

Created by YouthPLAYS' co-founders, Jonathan Dorf and Ed Shockley, ProduceaPlay.com serves as a resource for producers at all levels as it addresses the many facets of production. As Dorf and Shockley speak from their years of experience (as playwrights, producers, directors and more), they are joined by a group of award-winning theatre professionals and experienced teachers from the world of academic theatre, all making their expertise available for free in the hope of helping this and future generations of producers, whether it's at the school or university level, or in community or professional theatres.

The site is organized into a series of major topics, each of which has its own page that delves into the subject in detail, offering suggestions and links for further information. For example, Publicity covers everything from Publicizing Auditions to How to Use Social Media to Posters to whether it's worth hiring a publicist. Casting details Where to Find the Actors, How to Evaluate a Resume, Callbacks and even Dealing with Problem Actors. You'll find guidance on your Production Timeline, The Theater Space, Picking a Play, Budget, Contracts, Rehearsing the Play, The Program, House Management, Backstage, and many other important subjects.

The site is constantly under construction, so visit often for the latest insights on play producing, and let it help make your play production dreams a reality.

More from YouthPLAYS

Crossing the Threshold by Maura Campbell

Dramedy. 60-70 minutes. 6-10 males, 6-10 females (12-20 performers possible).

Fifteen-year-old Sarah grows up in the 1960s with cerebral palsy and just wants to be like everybody else. But between the mean girls at her boarding school and her cold and distant mother, she has given up on happiness. Then one day Sarah is given a half-starved Morgan horse who needs her as much as she needs him. Based on a true story, *Crossing the Threshold* is a moving and often comic play about one girl's fight to be whole, and the transcendental power of friendship.

The Old New Kid by Adam J. Goldberg

Comedy. 30-40 minutes. 2-9+ males, 3-10+ females (8-30+ performers possible).

It's the half-day of school before Thanksgiving break, and current "new kid" Alan Socrates Bama just wants to get through the day. But when a new-new kid arrives, things change. Alan has three hours to find the meaning of Thanksgiving, survive elementary school politics, battle for his identity, and spell the word "cornucopia" in this *Peanuts*-flavored comedy for kids of all ages.

Slow by Keegon Schuett

Drama. 45-55 minutes. 1 male, 3 females, 1 either.

Lizzy Slominski is better known to her classmates as "Camera Girl," because she's always hiding behind her digital camera snapping photos of strangers. Her days as a loner end when a mysterious new boy appears at the bus stop. Will she be able to put down her camera and connect, or is she doomed to a life of observing through the lens?

Techies by Don Goodrum
Comedy. 25-35 minutes. 5-6 males, 3-4 females (8-9 performers possible).

Overachieving high school senior Tony Sullivan just wants to get through one more production so that he can move on to Harvard and the rest of his life. But with overdramatic actors, overmedicated teachers and overprotective parents seemingly aligning to thwart his every move, will the show go on? Will Tony? A comic look at one of life's most important transitions and a loving tribute to the unsung heroes of the stage, the kids who sit in the dark and make the magic happen.

Scheme Space by Claudia Haas
Drama. 25-35 minutes. 2 males, 5 females.

The lives of seven teens collide when an inappropriate photo is put online. Soon, what starts out as a prank spirals out of control. Will this ill-conceived bid for popularity end up destroying friendships and even lives?

Two Dudes from Daytona by Matt Buchanan
Comedy. 55-65 minutes. 6-16+ males, 7-17+ females (15-30+ performers possible).

When best friends Val and Theo from Daytona Beach move to the Big Apple, Theo leaves behind the love of his life, Julia, and Val swears he'll never fall in love. Surprise, surprise, they both fall for the same girl in New York. Sylvia, an up-and-coming actress, loves Val, but Theo won't stop trying to cut his friend out. To make matters worse, her mother, who also happens to be Val's agent, is determined that she should marry the already successful Skip—whom she despises. And when Julia arrives, disguised as a boy, to find out why her lover hasn't been writing, mayhem ensues. But in the tradition of Shakespearean farce, all's well that ends well in this modern comedy loosely based on the Bard's *Two Gentlemen of Verona*.

17443583R00021

Made in the USA
Charleston, SC
11 February 2013